THE HAGGIS

ALEXANDER MACLEAN

Northern Books
from Famedram

FOREWORD

By Major-General K. C. Robertson-Urquhart, M.H.

THAT OF UNDERSTANDING, with complete sympathy, the various members of the animal kingdom, is a gift given to few men. The author of this short work on the Haggis is one so endowed.

Alexander MacLean makes a serious attempt to bring to the notice of the general public some of the little known facts concerning this unique animal. Keeping to facts, leaving fancy for the use of those who wish to scoff at Scotland's only true native species in the animal world, MacLean has in my opinion, performed a public service long overdue.

The immortal Robert Burns was the first man to pay due and just tribute to the haggis – and his birthday was January 25. Many years later on another January 25 the author of this present tribute was born in the county which shelters the home of the famous strain known as the Brindle haggis of Mull.

I am a lifelong supporter of all activities launched for the furtherance of the better understanding of the habits, needs and well-being of both the wild and domesticated haggis.

I deem it an honour to have been asked to write these few words. I trust the readers will enjoy the following pages and demand more from the pen of this dedicated man.

Signed,

Torlochy Castle,
Argyllshire.

K. C. Robertson-Urquhart

ISBN 0 905489 59 4 © Copyright Famedram Publishers Limited AB41 9EA
Printed by Kossuth Printing House Co 11-1106 Budapest.

CHAPTER 1

THE ORIGIN of the haggis (hagginasus) is lost in the mists of time – but there is no doubt about it being a purely Scottish beast. The animal was hunted by the ancient Picts and Scots, who used the Haggis Hound, a breed now extinct, to flush their prey from the cover of the heather.

In early times the young haggis was highly prized as part of the ancient peoples' diet. But because of its spectacular turn of speed in early life it is difficult to stalk and today the young animals are rarely killed for food. Present day preferences are for the more sophisticated taste of the adult animal's flesh.

One species only is found in the Isle of Mull – the brindle-coated haggis, the only long-haired variety. It is this particular strain which has given rise to many stories about the furiosity of these greatly misunderstood animals.

It is a little known fact that the adult haggis changes its sex every seven years. And few people are aware that it is this phenomenon which triggered off one of the most popular axioms of modern times.

Just before the haggis is about to change sex it suffers prolonged bouts of itching. The creatures can be observed rubbing themselves on any convenient protruberance. So we have the saying the 'seven year itch'.

The haggis was once a creature of the seas and lochs. Even to this day there are some haggis which have signs of what was once a dorsal fin.

The Institute of Grasspoint, Mull has the fossilised remains of a haggis which was fully aquatic. Cave drawings found on many of the Western Isles leave no doubt in the minds of scientists that the haggis did not become a land animal until early in the seventh century.

One group of research workers put forward the theory that the sounds heard by Mendelssohn on his visit to Fingal's Cave were made by the last remaining aquatic haggis, and not the waves of the sea.*

Signs of the dorsal fin are never found on any of the Mull haggis. These pure-bred animals living in an area of near-drought do, however, take to water with obvious enjoyment.

Added to the established fact that the haggis is purely Celtic in origin, it has been proved that it is a native of one particular part of Scotland – the Hebrides. Haggis did not appear on the mainland until the time of the invasion by the Norsemen.

These hungry men of the sea hunted and

*See the Kinglington Report The Origins of Sound. Revised edition

harried the animals to such an extent that many of them swam from island to island in an attempt to evade the hunters.

It was from the Isle of Mull that they reached the mainland by entering the sea at a spot just beyond Duart Point and, swimming first to the island of Kerrera, they reached the shores of Argyll at a point where Oban now stands.

The Mull haggis is without doubt the purest of all known strains, never having been crossed with animals from the mainland. This accounts for much of the fierceness found in the haggis living wild on the hills of Glen More, West Ardhu and Loch Buie. Research has shown that this is mainly due to the diet enjoyed by the Mull haggis.

The brindle haggis, already mentioned, is only found in Mull and is the most dangerous of all. It was this particular animal which enabled scientists to pinpoint diet as the main cause of aggressiveness.*

Another rare species worthy of mention is the Gunna haggis, The Isle of Gunna lies between Coll and Tiree. Owned by an animal lover, it is the haven of the most docile haggis of all.

Gunna is given over to the exclusive use of what we humans call the lesser animals. The Barnacle goose fertilises the island in the same way as the guan birds of South America deposit fertiliser on the Galapagos Islands. This results in Gunna having pastures unique in the Western world.

The lush green grass is known in the area as 'gentle grass' because of its delicate texture. The Gunna haggis thrive on their diet and, because of the abundance of natural fodder, never go hungry.

They are the only grass-eating haggis. It appears to be a case of well-fed, well-behaved. So, in an area of a few square miles, we have the most aggressive and the most docile of a species.

Islanders, fearing the extinction of the whole race at the time of the Covenanters, brought some of the Gunna stock over to Mull, where they hid them in caves.

*See White Paper Dietary Effects on Wild Animals, June 1947

Through great care and attention to detail they were able to encourage these docile creatures to breed in captivity. But not until they had thousands of healthy animals – and the caves were becoming crowded – did they inform the outside world of their success.

We who love the haggis – wild or domesticated – for its sheer beauty of form, its delightful habits, its grace of movement and its never-to-be-forgotten tweedy scent, owe these dedicated men and women a debt beyond our ken.

Praise to their memory!

ChAPTER 2

I N BOTH its wild and domesticated state the haggis is a clean living animal. One of the most moving sights still to be seen in the more remote parts of the Highlands is the bathing ritual of the wild haggis.

Professor William Lodge, the well-known naturalist and painter specialising in animal life, has caught the true beauty of the haggis during the performance of its ablutions in his celebrated picture – 'Pride of Mull' – which now hangs in the Beatty Room of the Highland Art Gallery at Pennyghael.

Professor Lodge, the only Englishman ever given membership of the Highland Guild, recently gave a lecture to a learned society of Dalnafidden based on his observations during the painting of the picture in Glen More. Permission to quote from the lecture notes was obtained just before the Professor left for Glenforsa in search of a suitable spot to build a hide for use in the painting of his next picture 'The Birth of a Wild Haggis'.

"The main bath of the day is taken at sunrise, with a second and less lengthy affair following during the early afternoon.

"The mother haggis appears first, just as the sun comes over the hill. Emerging from the cover of the heather, she stands for a moment while she sniffs, first up wind, then down. If danger is near she returns to cover and the bathing is delayed.

"On finding everything safe she moves nearer the loch, but first she looks right, then left, then right again. When all is clear she gives the lochan call.

(This call was incorporated in the pipe music composed by the late Pipe Major Archie MacLauderdale for the opening of the 1888 Exhibition of Scottish Scone Stones.)

"On hearing his mate's call, the male haggis, busy guarding the young, guides his charges to the waterside. While the parents watch the calves take their bath.

"The routine is strict and unchanging amongst all strains of haggis. Three complete immersions in all seasons – and then a return to the heather, where they proceed to dry themselves by rolling over and over.

"Once dry, the young lie still in the heather – a perfect hiding place for the calves. Thereafter the male takes his three dips, followed by his mate.

"Some idea of the inborn modesty of these delightful creatures can be gleaned from the fact that all young haggis, of both sexes and the father, or sire, turn their backs while the mother, or dam, takes her bath."

Having quoted Professor Lodge's account of the wild haggis taking its bath, it is essential to point out that the domestic haggis must be provided with pools of clear water if there is no natural loch near the ranch.
And the water must be clean. Even a young haggis about to take its first wash will only enter clear water.

All domestic drobhs* must be provided with an abundant supply of clean wheat straw to dry themselves on if there is no handy heather.

Unlike the Highland sheep, the haggis eats only once a day. This feast takes place just before sundown, and the fully grown animals, measuring twelve inches at the shoulder, will consume three times their own weight of white heather at one feeding.

The scarcity of white heather is due

* *Gaelic for drove, herd*

mainly to two factors – factors which underline the lack of white heather in the Isle of Mull, where the wild haggis is most numerous.

The wild haggis will only eat white heather* and this will only grow where a clansman of Clan MacLean shed his blood in defence of a just cause.**

The blood of the MacLeans is said to grow heated under such circumstances – to such an extent that, should one of them be wounded and his blood be spilled, it is so hot on reaching the ground that it blanches the purple heather. From that moment on, only white heather will grow at that spot.

It can be readily understood that one of the major problems facing the early breeders of domestic haggis was that of finding a suitable and acceptable diet. Heather is often hard to come by when one farms far from the hills.

In the spring of 1681 a certain Willie MacKinnon of Tobermory, in the north of Mull, brought home some bog cotton, which he used to plug his ears while his wife, Margaret Stewart MacKinnon, was learning the pipes under the tutorship of

* There is one exception – see Gunna haggis (hagginasus gunnensis).

* * The author merely quotes this as a local legend.

her brother, Donald Stewart of Mornish.

Willie brought about six months' supply and dumped it beside the byre where he housed his domestic drobh. After having his tea he came outside with the idea of taking the bog cotton to the fireside to dry out – and was surprised to find the haggis greedily chewing up his supply of earplugs.

Willie's discovery soon became known far and wide, and this is how the staple diet of the domestic species came to be known as 'MacKinnon's Meal'.

Wild Haggis sleep in a special formation made up of two circles. The whole drobh lie down together with the calves forming an inner circle. The adults then lie in an outer circle facing outwards. This is when the Haggis bird comes into its own.*

* See Birtle. Birds of the Northlands, *Chapter 7*

Like the Rhino bird, the so-called Haggis bird is small compared to the creature it spends its life with. The Haggis bird is smaller than the common Tit. Its plumage is brightly coloured.

During the day the bird rides perched on the back of its chosen haggis. Every haggis has a bird. During the heat of the day the bird sleeps and gathers strength for the labours of the night, when it acts as an early warning system to the drobh.

When the haggis have settled down for the night, the birds take up their guard. Observers believe they work some system of 'turn and turn about' as they do not all appear to be on guard at one and the same time.

For a brief spell around dawn the drobhs are left to their own devices, awake or asleep, for this is when the birds feed off the grubs found on the bracken fronds.

Though living out their lives with the haggis, the birds have a well-developed sense of smell which helps them in their guard duties. Their double inverted nostrils enable them to pick up a scent both up and down wind. But perhaps their most useful asset for guard duty is their infra-red optic nerve, which gives them perfect night vision.

When danger threatens the birds set up a screaming call – a call which, as yet, remains to be incorporated in the pipe music.

The sleeping habits of the domesticated haggis differ markedly from those of their wilder cousins. The domesticated haggis loves warmth while sleeping and, unlike the wild variety, never sleeps more than two together. When adult they pair male and female.

There is always a perfect balance in numbers, due to the strict supervision of the drobh leader when it comes time for any of his charges to change sex.

Domesticated haggis should never be allowed to live within the house. Even show specimens should not be encouraged to develop into house pets. The haggis,

once indoors, will soon find their way to the bedrooms – and once settled on a comfortable bed they can become quite savage when disturbed.

In addition, long periods of living indoors rob the animals of the natural oils required to keep their coats in good condition. When you see a haggis with blemishes on its skin – where the coat has become thin – you can be sure it has been allowed to live indoors far too long.

CHAPTER 3

THE FUTURE of the haggis is now assured. There is no danger of it becoming extinct now that the Highland Guild and other interested bodies have succeeded in establishing preserves where the animals can breed in their wild state and where the hunting of them is prohibited at all seasons.

The Commissioners control the numbers within these reservations and when well-defined limits are reached some of the animals are released for a life of complete freedom on the hill. It is from these that the hunter must find his prey. All attempts to set up hunting on a commercial basis have been banned.

A decision which the true haggis lover, be he Scots or of other nationality, will applaud with passion.

The people, and they are many, who maintain that the wild haggis makes better eating than that bred on the domestic ranches, must content themselves with limited supplies – but at least they are assured of prime specimens, thanks to the foresight of the true haggis lovers.

Demand for the haggis in markets outside Scotland is mainly met from the stocks of the domestic ranches. The volume of business now being transacted with almost every country in the world is fast approaching that enjoyed by the whisky industry.

No figures are available to show the value of haggis exports as a contribution to the national purse, but it is plain from the records of individual ranches that the Exchequer is reaping a goodly harvest.

The latest development in the haggis export field is American capital involvement in the promotion of a canning factory on Tayside. It appears there is a great demand for canned haggis on the North American continent. The continued approaches from high-class food stores led to this American company setting up business in Scotland.

Some years ago an American concern with large interests in the cattle ranches of the Middle West tried to obtain permission to import live haggis into America. The British Government of the day stood firm and refused their request.

It was this attempt by another country to introduce haggis on the hoof that led to the Member for Hammersmith Central introducing a Private Members' Bill to prohibit the export of live haggis.

Supported by the Guild and the Federation of Scottish Wild Life Development Societies, these organisations having many MPs in their ranks, the Bill went through without any opposition.

In recognition of his good work on behalf of the haggis being kept purely Scottish, Mr George R.A. Allan, the MP concerned, was presented with a parchment by the Guild. Further recognition was given by the setting up of an Allan Bursary at the Grasspoint Institute.

The wild haggis has always brought a high price in the markets of Scotland. Many years ago, when the animals were scarce, the cost of this essential food* was beyond the means of the average wage-earning Scot. It was at this time that the breeder of the domestic haggis began to flourish.

With the expense and time involved in hunting the wild species and also the growing demand from English markets, the domestic breeder was able to increase his drobhs and supply the needs of the housewife at a price within the reach of the great majority of haggis fanciers.

* See *Highland Customs and Diets*, Rod. Harper, Oban, 1897

The overheads in establishing a haggis ranch are low. In areas where bog cotton isplentiful the rancher's main outgoings are for wages of herdsmen, or drobhsmen as they are yet called in Mull – and a sum for the construction and maintenance of buildings.

There being no disease whatsoever amongst haggis, the breeder is not even faced with bills for veterinary attention and the costly vaccines used in the raising of sheep and cattle. In the field of agriculture and farming the haggis ranchers constitute the only group never to have asked for a Government subsidy.

As with the wild species, the best domesticated haggis are found on Mull. There are many ranches throughout the island, and some ranchers have established subsidiaries on the isles of Coll and Tiree.

The Tiree haggis is fast becoming a favourite in the English markets, where its more delicate flavour, due largely to the nature of the bog cotton growing in the island's sandy soil, pleases the English palate.

The haggis being, as it is, an original native of the Hebrides, it is only fitting that the leading breeders of the now popular domestic animal should be found in the Western Isles. The ranchers of Mull are thought by many to be the best.

They are certainly accepted as experts in every department of this most exacting type of farming. In great demand at the growing number of haggis shows, now part of every agricultural gathering in Scotland, the Mull men, called upon to perform the judging soon realised that the general public had but little knowledge of the haggis and the industry which has grown up over the last few generations.

By mutual agreement, the Mull ranchers opened their establishments to the public. And when visits to a haggis ranch became a must for tourists visiting Mull the ranchers on other islands and on the mainland soon followed suit.

May and October are the months of the haggis rutting seasons and, in the interests of public safety, the Commissioners have made it a rule at all ranches that the public should not be admitted at these times.

Visitors wishing to enter the confines of a haggis ranch near the times mentioned above should look out for the rutting warning flag. All ranches have their own particular flag – most based upon the rancher's tartan, with some embellishment added.

During rutting time flags are flown at

DO NOT open the gate
to the general public

RUTTING IN PROGRESS

half-mast. On no account should visitors enter
the confines of a ranch when the flag is in the
warning position. Even the tame domestic haggis
can be fierce when disturbed at this time. Apart
from the danger to humans, the effect on a haggis
forced to defend itself during such an intimate
time is catastrophic.

The animal never mates or breeds again.
And some chemical reaction set up within its
body by the disturbance causes the flesh to
harden. This results in a great loss to the

rancher, since the beast has to be disposed of at low prices for use as pet food.

With the growth of popularity of the haggis shows, the services of the professional handlers are in demand. In fact there is now a shortage of fully experienced men. The Professional Haggis Handlers' Association, only recently formed, is trying to raise money to set up a training school.

They have already acquired suitable premises on the outskirts of Perth. An appeal is shortly to be launched, and collections will be made at all shows during the season.

Next year it is hoped to stage the first ever Haggis Championship Show in England.

Arrangements are being made with a view to holding the event in Hyde Park and it is hoped that a national newspaper will provide sponsorship. The show would be certain to attract exhibitors from all over Scotland, providing as it would, such an excellent opportunity for them to gain publicity.

With the advent of haggis shows and the increasing demand for first class stock, the Commissioners have started a stud book and register of pedigree.

These are housed in Tobermory and may be inspected by breeders and members of the public on completion of an application form – obtainable from the office on Main Street.

So the future is bright. Scotland – the world, in fact, – can look forward to the greater development of the haggis industry. An industry which, coupled with nature's own supreme contribution in the form of the wild haggis, provides not only sustenance, but gives pleasure to the active hunter and to those who take their recreation in the more peaceful manner, as a spectator at a show.

The author has been approached by many people asking if factory farming methods have spread to the haggis ranches.

The short answer is – no. The Commissioners meeting in Inverness during the past year revised the rules of breeding, which now prohibit such a system being introduced.

Increasing pressure of demand must be met by an increase in the size of drobhs, and the setting up of more ranches.

The Commissioners have given strength to the cause of the haggis rancher who has been in open competition with the Forestry Commission in the taking over of land when it comes on to the market.

With the future of natural farming methods assured, the ranchers can afford to pay top prices for land. It is a sign of the healthy state of the industry that these hardworking men can do this without any question of them asking for grants or loans from the Government or semi-official bodies.

––––––––––––––––––

Having reached the end of this little booklet it is hoped the reader will now have a greater interest in the haggis as an animal of great charm, as well as an item of diet greatly beneficial to the health of all who partake of the delicacy.